■SCHOLASTIC

TIMES TABLES

PRACTICE BOOK

AGES 9–11

Be a times tables master

Scholastic Education, an imprint of Scholastic Ltd
Book End, Range Road, Witney, Oxfordshire, OX29 0YD
Registered office: Westfield Road, Southam, Warwickshire CV47 0RA
www.scholastic.co.uk

British Library Cataloguing-in-Publication Data
A catalogue record for this book is available from the British Library.
ISBN 978-1407-18246-9
Printed by Bell & Bain

Author
Paul Hollin
Editorial team
Rachel Morgan, Shannon Keenlyside, Audrey Stokes, Helen Lewis
and Julia Roberts
Cover and Series Design
Scholastic Design Team: Nicolle Thomas, Neil Salt and Alice Duggan
Illustration
Matt Ward @ Beehive Illustration

Contents

How to use this book

Rapid recall of times tables facts up to 12 × 12 by the end of Year 4 is a key expectation for all children in England. In fact, so key that all children will sit a Times Tables Check at the end of Year 4 from 2020.

Why are the times tables important?

They support mathematical learning and understanding. If you know your times tables, this frees up space to learn and work on new mathematical concepts and problems. And, as you know, we use them all the time in daily life, for example we use them when working out costs, doubling recipes or finding out how much we will need of something (for example, *we need to put 6 chairs at each of the 8 tables. 8 × 6, we'll need 48 chairs*).

How does *Times Tables* help children master multiplication?

This *Practice Book* aims to give children the chance to practise their times tables, deepening their understanding as well as increasing their rapid recall. This means they understand the 'how and why' of multiplication as well as being able to answer multiplication facts quickly. They will understand, for example:

- ▶ You can multiply two numbers in any order and the answer will be the same:
  If you know 2 × 5 = 10, then you know 5 × 2 = 10.

- ▶ You can break up a multiplication fact:
  Don't remember 6 × 4? What if you think about it as 4 × 4 + 2 × 4?

- ▶ Multiplication is repeated addition:
  7 × 2 = 2 + 2 + 2 + 2 + 2 + 2 + 2
  8 × 2 = 2 + 2 + 2 + 2 + 2 + 2 + 2 + 2
  This means that if you know that 7 × 2 = 14, then 8 × 2 will be two more.

How can you help?

- ▶ Encourage short bursts of practice. Focus on a couple of tables in the first instance and move on to others once your child is confident.

- ▶ Talk about the times tables. Encourage your child to think about what they know and explain their thinking. You'll have opportunities to do this throughout this *Practice Book* as well.

- ▶ Look for real-life situations for your child to use the times tables. Seeing how you use what you know and showing off what you already know is a great motivator.

- ▶ Remind your child that our brains are growing when we make mistakes. Celebrate this growth!

- ▶ Speed may be important but can also cause many children anxiety. Focus on understanding multiplication and rehearsing the times tables in fun ways. Speed will come in time!

Track your progress online using our *free* Times Tables Check:
www.scholastic.co.uk/timestables

Advice for children

This book is full of practice questions and activities to help you master your times tables.

Each unit focuses on a different topic or times table.

This box helps you review a topic before you get practising.

Work through the questions in order.

Explaining helps you understand. Be sure to share what you know with a friend or an adult.

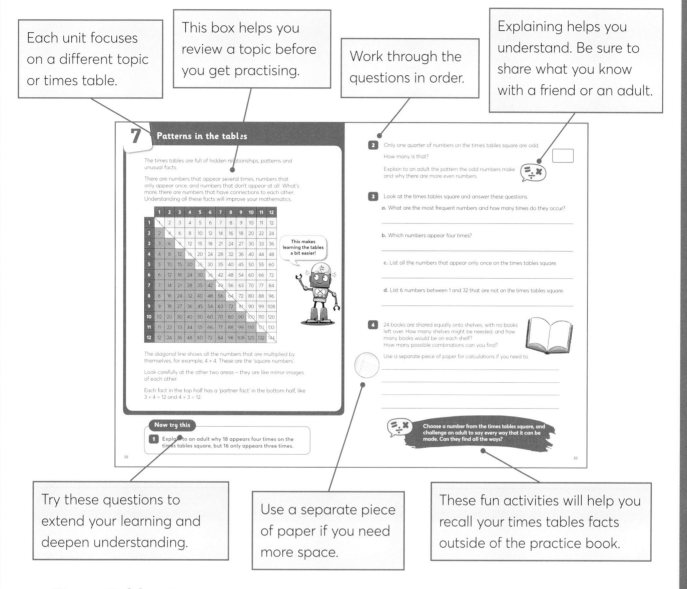

Try these questions to extend your learning and deepen understanding.

Use a separate piece of paper if you need more space.

These fun activities will help you recall your times tables facts outside of the practice book.

Times Tables tips

▶ Don't rush through the units. Concentrate on one unit at a time. Record your progress using the chart on page 45.

▶ Celebrate what you already know and think more deeply about it.

▶ Challenge yourself to master any parts you find tricky. Make your brain grow!

▶ Use equipment or draw pictures to help you. They are fantastic tools!

▶ Focus on memorising one or two times tables at a time. Master them, then move on to new ones.

▶ Times tables speed is great, but understanding is best.

▶ Look for opportunities to use your times tables every day, for example work out how many minutes you spend each week brushing your teeth.

▶ Keep trying. Keep thinking and exploring. You can do it!

1 Multiplication

Multiplication is a quick way to do repeated addition.

Each egg box contains six eggs, so in four boxes we have
6 + 6 + 6 + 6 = 24 eggs.

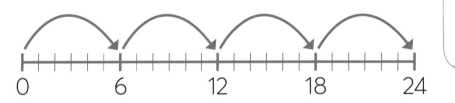

You can count in steps of six.

This works well for smaller amounts, but what if we have twelve boxes of eggs? We can count on 6 twelve times, or we can say '12 times 6'!

To make it even easier we use a multiplication sign to write the repeated addition as a multiplication sentence: 12 × 6

And that's where the times tables come in. These are all the different multiplications that are possible up to 12 times 12. Mastering these is your key to mathematical success.

1 Write each of these repeated additions as a multiplication sentence with the answer.

a. 4 + 4 + 4: _____

b. 8 + 8 + 8 + 8 + 8: _____

2 Sita says that understanding multiplication as repeated addition helps you to work out multiplication facts you cannot recall. Can you explain her thinking? Use an example to help you.

_____

_____

Arrays are useful for solving problems.

12 tins can be arranged in two rows of six (2 × 6 = 12).

Now try this

3 Try drawing different arrays to show how else you could arrange 12 tins.

Which times tables facts have you used?

4 Write this array as a multiplication sentence.

_____

The times tables square

	1	2	3	4	5	6	7	8	9	10	11	12
1	1	2	3	4	5	6	7	8	9	10	11	12
2	2	4	6	8	10	12	14	16	18	20	22	24
3	3	6	9	12	15	18	21	24	27	30	33	36
4	4	8	12	16	20	24	28	32	36	40	44	48
5	5	10	15	20	25	30	35	40	45	50	55	60
6	6	12	18	24	30	36	42	48	54	60	66	72
7	7	14	21	28	35	42	49	56	63	70	77	84
8	8	16	24	32	40	48	56	64	72	80	88	96
9	9	18	27	36	45	54	63	72	81	90	99	108
10	10	20	30	40	50	60	70	80	90	100	110	120
11	11	22	33	44	55	66	77	88	99	110	121	132
12	12	24	36	48	60	72	84	96	108	120	132	144

A times tables square can be used to find times tables facts. Have a go at finding 3 × 2 and 9 × 6.

Choose a times table then practise counting in steps to say every number in that table on the times tables square.

Just as the opposite of addition is subtraction, so the opposite of multiplication is division.

We say that division is the **inverse** of multiplication.

Here's an example:

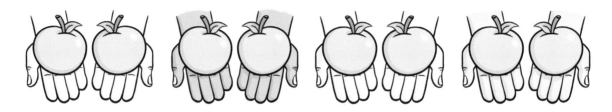

If 4 children each have 2 apples, there are 8 apples altogether.

The multiplication is | 4 × 2 = 8 |

Or we can look at it another way:
If 8 apples are shared equally between 4 children, they will each get 2 apples.

The division is | 8 ÷ 4 = 2 |

Notice that division is the inverse of multiplication. We can use one to check the other.

1 **a.** A teacher has 12 books and shares them equally between 3 children. How many books do they get each?

| | books

b. 20 sheep are divided equally into 2 fields. How many sheep are there in each field?

| | sheep

2 Choose the correct calculation (multiplication or division) to solve each of these problems.

    a. 3 horses all need 4 new horseshoes fitted.
    How many horseshoes will be needed altogether?

horseshoes

    b. 40 people go into a cinema.
    If there are 4 rows and the same number of people sit in
    each row, how many people will there be in each row?

people

3 Another, another, another! Write more calculations for each number in the centre.

$5 \times 3 =$

15

$\div 3 = 5$

Use the inverse
calculation to check
your answers!

21

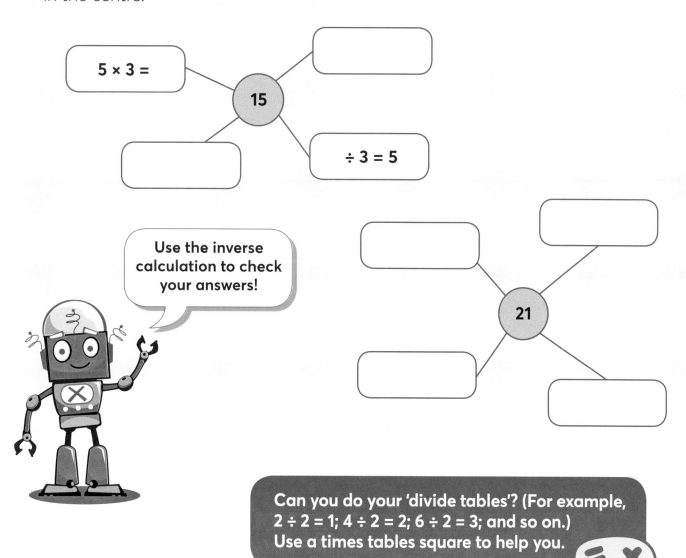

Can you do your 'divide tables'? (For example,
$2 \div 2 = 1$; $4 \div 2 = 2$; $6 \div 2 = 3$; and so on.)
Use a times tables square to help you.

These are three of the easiest tables to learn.

Write out the 2-times table up to 24 on a piece of paper:

$$1 × 2 = \qquad 2 × 2 = \qquad 3 × 2 = \qquad ...$$

What patterns do you notice?

Do you think the patterns continue beyond 24?

What patterns do you see for the 5- and 10-times tables?

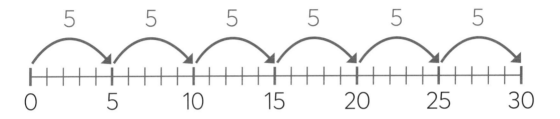

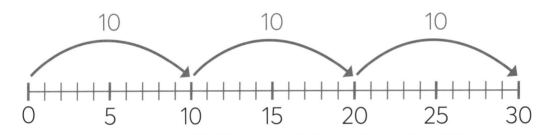

Notice that 4 × 5 is the same as 2 × 10. What would 8 × 5 be equivalent to?

1 Fill in the missing multiples:

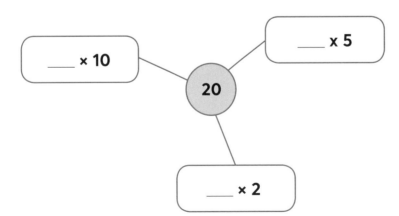

2 Investigate which numbers these times tables have in common on the times tables square.

    a. 2- and 5-times tables   c. 5- and 10-times tables

    b. 2- and 10-times tables   d. 2-, 5- and 10-times tables

3 In the Evens Stevens football league, teams get 10 points for winning, 5 points for a draw, and 2 points for losing.

The table shows the results at the end of the season.

Team	Games won	Games drawn	Games lost
United	4	7	6
Rovers	5	5	7
City	3	6	8
Rangers	4	8	5
Albion	5	1	11

Which team will be top of the league? _____

Which team will be bottom of the league? _____

How many more points do the top team have than the bottom team?

Use separate paper for calculations if you need to.

We have seen that the 5-times table is double the 10-times table. Can you find a link between the 2-times table and another table?

There are lots of links between these three times tables. After all, 3, 6, 9 are the first three multiples in the 3-times table.

Look at the 100 square below. Some multiples of 3 have a circle around them, some multiplies of 6 have a square around them, and some multiples of 9 have a cross on them. Can you finish the patterns all the way to 100?

1	2	③	4	5	⬛6	7	8	⊗9	10
11	⬛12	13	14	15	16	17	✕18	19	20
21	22	23	24	25	26	27	28	29	30
31	32	33	34	35	36	37	38	39	40
41	42	43	44	45	46	47	48	49	50
51	52	53	54	55	56	57	58	59	60
61	62	63	64	65	66	67	68	69	70
71	72	73	74	75	76	77	78	79	80
81	82	83	84	85	86	87	88	89	90
91	92	93	94	95	96	97	98	99	100

What do you notice?

1 Fill in the gaps:

a.

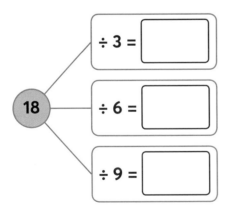

18

÷ 3 =

÷ 6 =

÷ 9 =

b.

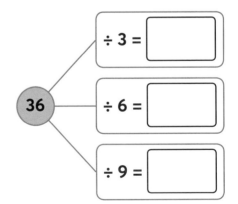

36

÷ 3 =

÷ 6 =

÷ 9 =

Now try this

2 Look back at the 100 square and question 1 on page 12.
What patterns do you notice in the 3-, 6- and 9-times tables?

3 Meet the aliens from planets Bim, Bam and Bom.

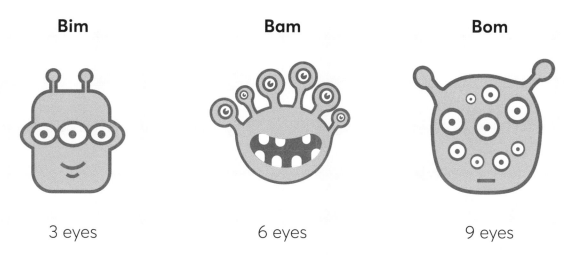

Bim	**Bam**	**Bom**
3 eyes	6 eyes	9 eyes

Unfortunately all the aliens are very short-sighted, so there is a great trade in contact lenses between the three planets!

The inter-galactic contact lens supplier has 300 lenses available today. How can he make sure the same number of aliens on each planet gets the lenses they need?

Explain your recommendations here. Use separate paper for calculations.

_____

_____

_____

Now try this

4 Explain this statement:
$12 \times 3 = 6 \times 6 = 3 \times 12$

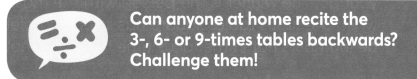

Can anyone at home recite the
3-, 6- or 9-times tables backwards?
Challenge them!

Turning the tables

This is a game for 2 players.

You will need:

two different-coloured pencils and some small pieces of paper.

	1	2	3	4	5	6	7	8	9	10	11	12
1	1	2	3	4	5	6	7	8	9	10	11	12
2	2	4	6	8	10	12	14	16	18	20	22	24
3	3	6	9	12	15	18	21	24	27	30	33	36
4	4	8	12	16	20	24	28	32	36	40	44	48
5	5	10	15	20	25	30	35	40	45	50	55	60
6	6	12	18	24	30	36	42	48	54	60	66	72
7	7	14	21	28	35	42	49	56	63	70	77	84
8	8	16	24	32	40	48	56	64	72	80	88	96
9	9	18	27	36	45	54	63	72	81	90	99	108
10	10	20	30	40	50	60	70	80	90	100	110	120
11	11	22	33	44	55	66	77	88	99	110	121	132
12	12	24	36	48	60	72	84	96	108	120	132	144

- The aim is to colour in the most squares from the 2-, 3-, 5-, 6-, 9- and 10-times tables.

- Place 6 pieces of paper numbered 2, 3, 5, 6, 9 and 10 in one pile. Then 12 pieces in another pile numbered 1 to 12.

- Shuffle the piles of paper and put them face down. Agree if you are reading the times tables square across or down.

- Take turns to pick one piece of paper from each pile (for example, 3 and 11). Using your coloured pencil, colour in the 33 square, then replace the pieces of paper at the bottom of the correct piles. The next player then takes two pieces of paper. If you get a calculation that is in two of the focus tables (for example, 2 × 5 or 5 × 2) colour in both squares.

- If you pick up numbers for a square that is already coloured in, miss your go. The winner is the person with the most squares coloured in when the times tables square has been completed as much as it can be (numbers not in the focus time tables cannot be coloured in).

Mixed tables test: 2, 3, 5, 6, 9, 10

These tests check your knowledge of all the times tables.

Use your tables skills wisely!

TEST 1

a. $2 \times 6 = \boxed{}$

b. $2 \times 8 = \boxed{}$

c. $6 \times \boxed{} = 30$

d. $10 \times 9 = \boxed{}$

e. $5 \times 3 = \boxed{}$

f. $6 \times 1 = \boxed{}$

g. $3 \times \boxed{} = 24$

h. $10 \times \boxed{} = 100$

i. $2 \times \boxed{} = 8$

j. $3 \times 4 = \boxed{}$

k. $5 \times \boxed{} = 35$

l. $3 \times \boxed{} = 36$

TEST 2

a. $10 \times \boxed{} = 50$

b. $3 \times 11 = \boxed{}$

c. $2 \times \boxed{} = 20$

d. $2 \times \boxed{} = 6$

e. $10 \times 4 = \boxed{}$

f. $9 \times \boxed{} = 36$

g. $5 \times \boxed{} = 25$

h. $6 \times 6 = \boxed{}$

i. $9 \times 5 = \boxed{}$

j. $6 \times \boxed{} = 18$

k. $6 \times 8 = \boxed{}$

l. $9 \times 12 = \boxed{}$

TEST 3

a. $\boxed{} \times 9 = 81$

b. $5 \times 8 = \boxed{}$

c. $\boxed{} \times 11 = 22$

d. $3 \times \boxed{} = 18$

e. $3 \times 9 = \boxed{}$

f. $5 \times \boxed{} = 20$

g. $\boxed{} \times 3 = 30$

h. $9 \times 6 = \boxed{}$

i. $\boxed{} \times 12 = 72$

j. $2 \times 12 = \boxed{}$

k. $5 \times \boxed{} = 60$

l. $\boxed{} \times 12 = 120$

Revising the 4-, 8- and 12-times tables

If you look carefully, there are patterns that can help you with these three times tables.

Look at the numbers in the 4-, 8- and 12-times tables below. Notice how the digits in the 1s place for the first 5 multiples are repeated in the next 5 multiples.

	1	2	3	4	5	6	7	8	9	10	11	12
4	4	8	12	16	20	24	28	32	36	40	44	48
8	8	16	24	32	40	48	56	64	72	80	88	96
12	12	24	36	48	60	72	84	96	108	120	132	144

So, 2 × 4 and 7 × 4 will have the same number of 1s.

$$2 \times 4 = \underline{8}$$ $$7 \times 4 = 2\underline{8}$$

The key fact to learn in each table is the multiple of 5.
5 × 4 = 20; 5 × 8 = 40; 5 × 12 = 60. Can you see why?

The questions below will help you to see this.

1 Complete the multiples:

a. 4, 8, 12, 16, 20, ⬜, ⬜, ⬜, ⬜, ⬜

b. 8, 16, 24, 32, 40, ⬜, ⬜, ⬜, ⬜, ⬜

c. 12, 24, 36, 48, 60, ⬜, ⬜, ⬜, ⬜, ⬜

2 Investigate which numbers these times tables have in common.

a. 4- and 8-times tables: _____

b. 4- and 12-times tables: _____

c. 8- and 12-times tables: _____

3 A friend is struggling to recall the 8-times table but tells you they are confident with the 4-times tables. What could you tell them and show them about the relationship between these times tables to help them?

> **Copy the 4- and 8-times tables to help you.**

_____

_____

_____

4 Mary collects seashells and sells them from her shop by the seaside.

One day Mary sells £216 worth of shells.

Find out how many small, medium and large shells she must have sold. There is more than one possible answer. The easiest way is to sell the same number of each shell. Try to find other ways that have different numbers of shells.

small shells
£4

medium shells
£8

large shells
£12

Use a separate piece of paper for your calculations and record your combinations.

> **Play Bing, Bang, Bong! Recite the 4-times table as fast as you can. If a number can also be divided by 8 shout 'Bang!'; if a number can also be divided by 12 shout 'Bong!'; if a number can be divided by 8 and 12 shout 'Bing Bang Bong!'.**

6 | Revising the 7- and 11-times tables

You have to feel a bit sorry for the 7- and 11-times tables. They really don't have much in common with other times tables.

Look at the multiples of 11 below. Can you see why they are quite easy to learn? What about the higher numbers?

	1	2	3	4	5	6	7	8	9	10	11	12
1	1	2	3	4	5	6	7	8	9	10	11	12
2	2	4	6	8	10	12	14	16	18	20	22	24
3	3	6	9	12	15	18	21	24	27	30	33	36
4	4	8	12	16	20	24	28	32	36	40	44	48
5	5	10	15	20	25	30	35	40	45	50	55	60
6	6	12	18	24	30	36	42	48	54	60	66	72
7	7	14	21	28	35	42	49	56	63	70	77	84
8	8	16	24	32	40	48	56	64	72	80	88	96
9	9	18	27	36	45	54	63	72	81	90	99	108
10	10	20	30	40	50	60	70	80	90	100	110	120
11	11	22	33	44	55	66	77	88	99	110	121	132
12	12	24	36	48	60	72	84	96	108	120	132	144

Now look at the multiples of 7. These are harder to learn; there is no pattern, but there are methods that help.

- You already know that $1 \times 7 = 7$, and that $10 \times 7 = 70$.

- If you learn a few other facts you can use them to find more:

- So, if we learn: $3 \times 7 = 21$, $5 \times 7 = 35$, and that $7 \times 7 = 49$ we can use these to work out others:

Not sure what 4 7s are? It is $3 \times 7 + 7$; $21 + 7 = 28$.

Not sure about 9×7? Do $10 \times 7 - 7 = 63$.

1 Complete the multiples:

a. 7, 14, ☐ , ☐ , ☐ , ☐ , ☐ , ☐ , ☐ ,

☐ , ☐ , ☐ ,

b. 11, 22, ☐ , ☐ , ☐ , ☐ , ☐ , ☐ , ☐ ,

☐ , ☐ , ☐ ,

Now try this

2 Sami says none of the numbers in 7- and 11-times tables appear anywhere else in the times tables square.
Is he correct? Explain your reasoning to an adult.

3 The schools in a local area take part in a competition every year.

Each school has to send an **equal number of teams** for football and netball. Football teams have 11 players; netball teams have 7 players.

If a school has 40 children, they could have two football and two netball teams, with 4 children left over (22 + 14 + 4 = 40).

If a school has 200 children, how many football teams and netball teams could they send?

Give your answer as a full sentence.

_____

_____

_____

_____

Use separate paper for calculations if you need to.

Work with an adult to learn the facts for the 7- and 11-times tables. Over a week, when one of you walks into a room that the other is in, the person in the room shouts a fact, such as '5 7s'! Get it right to score a point. Get it wrong, or hesitate, and you lose a point.

Goodies and baddies

1	2	3	4	5	6	7	8	9	10
11	12	13	14	15	16	17	18	19	20
21	22	23	24	25	26	27	28	29	30
31	32	33	34	35	36	37	38	39	40
41	42	43	44	45	46	47	48	49	50
51	52	53	54	55	46	57	58	59	60
61	62	63	64	65	66	67	68	69	70
71	72	73	74	75	76	77	78	79	80
81	82	83	84	85	86	87	88	89	90
91	92	93	94	95	96	97	98	99	100

This is a game for 2 players.

You will need:

a different-coloured counter for each player, and one 6-sided dice.

The first player to get from 1, all the way to 100 or beyond, is the winner.

- Any number that can be divided by 4, 8 or 12 is a **goodie**. Any number that can be divided by 7 or 11 is a **baddie**.

- Players take turns to roll the dice and move that number of squares. Some squares are special and things happen if a player lands on one of them:

  - For a multiple of 4: move forward 1 extra square.

  - For a multiple of 8: move forward 3 extra squares.

  - For a multiple of 12: move forward 5 extra squares.

  - For a square that can be divided by 4, 8 and 12: move forward 10 extra squares.

  - For a square that is a multiple of 7 or 11, move back 10 squares.

  - If a player lands on 77 (a multiple of 7 and 11): go back to the start.

  - For squares that can be divided by 4, 8 or 12 *and* 7 or 11 (such as 28 which can be divided by 4 and 7), nothing happens.

Mixed tables test: 4, 7, 8, 11, 12

Look for links with the 4-, 8- and 12-times tables.

TEST 1

a. 4 × 6 = ☐

b. 8 × ☐ = 24

c. 8 × 4 = ☐

d. 7 × 9 = ☐

e. 7 × ☐ = 49

f. 8 × 8 = ☐

g. 4 × ☐ = 48

h. 7 × ☐ = 42

i. 11 × ☐ = 121

j. 11 × 1 = ☐

k. 12 × ☐ = 84

l. 12 × 3 = ☐

TEST 2

a. 7 × ☐ = 35

b. 8 × ☐ = 40

c. 7 × 3 = ☐

d. 12 × ☐ = 96

e. 8 × ☐ = 88

f. 4 × 10 = ☐

g. 4 × 9 = ☐

h. 11 × 9 = ☐

i. 4 × ☐ = 12

j. 12 × 5 = ☐

k. 8 × 10 = ☐

l. 11 × ☐ = 44

TEST 3

a. ☐ × 7 = 28

b. 11 × ☐ = 77

c. 12 × 2 = ☐

d. ☐ × 3 = 33

e. 7 × 2 = ☐

f. ☐ × 8 = 56

g. 8 × 6 = ☐

h. 12 × ☐ = 72

i. ☐ × 10 = 70

j. ☐ × 9 = 72

k. 4 × ☐ = 20

l. 11 × 12 = ☐

Patterns in the tables

The times tables are full of hidden relationships, patterns and unusual facts.

There are numbers that appear several times, numbers that only appear once, and numbers that don't appear at all. What's more, there are numbers that have connections to each other. Understanding all these facts will improve your mathematics.

	1	2	3	4	5	6	7	8	9	10	11	12
1	1	2	3	4	5	6	7	8	9	10	11	12
2	2	4	6	8	10	12	14	16	18	20	22	24
3	3	6	9	12	15	18	21	24	27	30	33	36
4	4	8	12	16	20	24	28	32	36	40	44	48
5	5	10	15	20	25	30	35	40	45	50	55	60
6	6	12	18	24	30	36	42	48	54	60	66	72
7	7	14	21	28	35	42	49	56	63	70	77	84
8	8	16	24	32	40	48	56	64	72	80	88	96
9	9	18	27	36	45	54	63	72	81	90	99	108
10	10	20	30	40	50	60	70	80	90	100	110	120
11	11	22	33	44	55	66	77	88	99	110	121	132
12	12	24	36	48	60	72	84	96	108	120	132	144

This makes learning the tables a bit easier!

The diagonal line shows all the numbers that are multiplied by themselves, for example, 4×4. These are the 'square numbers'.

Look carefully at the other two areas – they are like mirror images of each other.

Each fact in the top half has a 'partner fact' in the bottom half, like $3 \times 4 = 12$ and $4 \times 3 = 12$.

Now try this

1 Explain to an adult why 18 appears four times on the times tables square, but 16 only appears three times.

2 Only one quarter of numbers on the times tables square are odd.

How many is that?

Explain to an adult the pattern the odd numbers make and why there are more even numbers.

3 Look at the times tables square and answer these questions.

a. What are the most frequent numbers and how many times do they occur?

_____

b. Which numbers appear four times?

_____

c. List all the numbers that appear only once on the times tables square.

_____

d. List 6 numbers between 1 and 32 that are not on the times tables square.

_____

4 24 books are shared equally onto shelves, with no books left over. How many shelves might be needed, and how many books would be on each shelf?
How many possible combinations can you find?

Use a separate piece of paper for calculations if you need to.

_____

_____

_____

_____

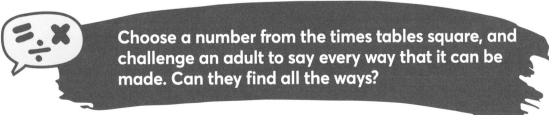

Choose a number from the times tables square, and challenge an adult to say every way that it can be made. Can they find all the ways?

8 Number walls

Number walls are a useful way of understanding why different times tables sometimes have the same numbers in them.

For example, take this number wall.

2	2	2	2	2	2
3		3		3		3
4		4		4

You can see quickly that 6 × 2 is equivalent to 4 × 3, which are also equivalent to 3 lots of 4.

You can also see that 2 × 2 is equivalent to 1 × 4; 3 × 2 equals 2 × 3; and that 4 × 2 equals 2 × 4.

---

1 Find as many equivalent multiplication facts as you can on this number wall:

12 × 2; [ ] ; [ ] ; [ ] ; [ ] ; [ ]

2	2	2	2	2	2	2	2	2	2	2	2
3		3		3		3		3		3		3		3
4		4		4		4		4		4
6		6		6		6
8		8		8
12		12

Now try this

2 Use a blank piece of paper and draw a number wall to 20 for the 2-, 5- and 10-times tables.

3 A decorator has been asked to create a border for a bathroom wall using different-sized tiles. The border must be 48cm long and 4cm high.
(Tip: 48 = 4 × 12)

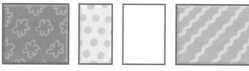

- He uses tiles in different lengths.

- All the tiles are 1cm high.

- He can use as many tiles as he wants.

- Only one type of tile can be used in each row and rows cannot be repeated.

- He can only put shorter tiles on top of longer ones.

- He cannot put the same length tile on top of each other.

- Look at the chart and plan the tiles for the border.

Tile length	2cm	3cm	4cm	6cm	8cm	12cm
Cost per tile	£5	£6	£7	£8	£9	£10

Choose which type of tiles the decorator needs, and how many of each type. To finish, calculate how much the border will cost.

Can you find the cheapest and most expensive solutions?

Explain your findings here. Use separate paper for calculations if you need to.

_____

_____

_____

_____

Work with an adult or a friend. Shout a multiplication fact at them; they have to shout a connected fact back.
How many facts can you shout out between you?
Note how many, and then try to break your record the next day.

Factors are numbers that divide exactly into a larger number.

4 and 5 are factors of 20. They are a factor pair.

Multiples are numbers that are made by multiplying a number.

20 is a multiple of 4. It is also a multiple of 5.

Every number on the times tables square is made by multiplying two numbers together.

> This square shows us that 4 × 5 = 20, and that 5 × 4 = 20.

	1	**2**	**3**	**4**	**5**
1	1	2	3	4	5
2	2	4	6	8	10
3	3	6	9	12	15
4	4	8	12	16	(20)
5	5	10	15	(20)	25

So we can say that 4 and 5 are factors of 20. They are a factor pair because they multiply together to make 20.

If you look at a larger times tables square (for example on page 7), you will see that 20 has another factor pair: 2 and 10.

2, 4, 5 and 10 are all factors of 20. 1 and 20 are also factors of 20, but they don't appear on the grid.

> We can say that 20 is a common multiple of 1, 2, 4, 5, 10 and 20.

1 For each pair of numbers, circle the odd one out that is not a common multiple of the numbers in bold:

a. **2, 4:**   8   12   22   28

b. **3, 7:**   21   35   42   63

c. **6, 10:**   30   60   90   110

d. **8, 12:**   24   56   72   96

e. **3, 11:**   33   66   88   132

f. **4, 6:**   12   18   24   48

2 Write all the factor pairs between 1 and 12 that you can find for each of these numbers.

a. 6: _____

b. 11: _____

c. 15: _____

d. 16: _____

e. 30: _____

f. 48: _____

g. 60: _____

h. 99: _____

3 Find all of the numbers on the times tables square between 20 and 30 that have only one factor pair from 1 to 12.

_____

Now try this

4 Investigate which numbers on the times tables square have the most factor pairs between 1 and 12.

Why do some numbers have fewer factors than others?

Roll two dice and use the numbers to make as many correct mathematical statements linked to multiplication as possible. For example,

'3 4s are 12'
'3 is a factor of 12'
'4 is a factor of 12'
'3 and 4 are a factor pair of 12'
'12 is a common multiple of 3 and 4'.

10 Squares and primes

Square numbers

When we multiply a number by itself we get its square.

For example, $5 \times 5 = 25$. We say five squared is 25.

This can be written like this: $5^2 = 25$.

Look at the array – can you see 3^2 and 5^2?
What about 4^2? Can you see any other squares?

Prime numbers

Prime numbers can only be divided by themselves or 1.

1 itself is not a prime number, and 2 is the only even prime number.

---

1 Every times table has a square number in it.
Complete the grid. The first one has been done for you:

Times table	Square	Using ^{2}	=
1-times table	1×1	1^2	1
2-times table			
3-times table			
4-times table			
5-times table			
6-times table			
7-times table			
8-times table			
9-times table			
10-times table			
11-times table			
12-times table			

2 Look at a times tables square, for example on page 7.
What do you notice about the pattern of the square numbers?

3 Cross out number 1 in the number grid below.
Do not cross out numbers 2, 3, 5 or 7.

1	2	3	4	5	6	7	8	9	10
11	12	13	14	15	16	17	18	19	20
21	22	23	24	25	26	27	28	29	30
31	32	33	34	35	36	37	38	39	40
41	42	43	44	45	46	47	48	49	50
51	52	53	54	55	56	57	58	59	60
61	62	63	64	65	66	67	68	69	70
71	72	73	74	75	76	77	78	79	80
81	82	83	84	85	86	87	88	89	90
91	92	93	94	95	96	97	98	99	100

Starting from number 4, cross out all the multiples of 2.

Next, cross out all the multiples of 3. Then cross out all the multiples of 5.

Finally, cross out all the multiples of 7. What do you notice?

_____

_____

4 Extend the grid to help you
find the next four prime
numbers. What are they?

_____

Play True or False. Ask someone
to give you a number between
1 and 100. Say 'True' if it is a prime
number and 'False' if it is not.
Then share a fact to prove it.

12-minute times tables

This is a game for 2 players.

You will need:

two different-coloured pencils; two 6-sided dice; a timer

	1	2	3	4	5	6	7	8	9	10	11	12
1												
2												
3												
4												
5												
6												
7												
8												
9												
10												
11												
12												

Take turns to roll the two dice. You may either:

- Write both the products of the two numbers you roll, for example if you roll 4 and 5, write 20 twice.

- Double the value of one or both of the dice then find their product, for example double 4 is 8 and double 5 is 10, 8 × 10 = 80 so write in 80 in both squares.

- Whoever has the most numbers written in 12 minutes wins.

Mixed tables test: all tables

Don't just try to remember facts, think about what you know.

TEST 1

a. 4 × 8 = ☐

b. 6 × ☐ = 42

c. 9 × 7 = ☐

d. 2 × 7 = ☐

e. 9 × ☐ = 72

f. 8 × 2 = ☐

g. 4 × ☐ = 8

h. 5 × ☐ = 30

i. 12 × ☐ = 144

j. 8 × 1 = ☐

k. 11 × 2 = ☐

l. 10 × ☐ = 60

TEST 2

a. 4 × ☐ = 16

b. 5 × 9 = ☐

c. 12 × ☐ = 48

d. 3 × ☐ = 21

e. 12 × 10 = ☐

f. 1 × ☐ = 12

g. 8 × ☐ = 56

h. 7 × 12 = ☐

i. 2 × ☐ = 18

j. 12 × 11 = ☐

k. 6 × 4 = ☐

l. 3 × 3 = ☐

TEST 3

a. ☐ ÷ 6 = 9

b. 15 ÷ ☐ = 5

c. 12 ÷ 2 = ☐

d. ☐ ÷ 11 = 7

e. ☐ ÷ 9 = 12

f. 28 ÷ 7 = ☐

g. 110 ÷ ☐ = 11

h. ☐ ÷ 11 = 9

i. 7 ÷ ☐ = 7

j. ☐ ÷ 1 = 5

k. 96 ÷ 12 = ☐

l. ☐ ÷ 9 = 3

11 Multiplying powers of 10

If we multiply by a power of 10 we change the place value of the numbers:

| 2 × 10 = 20 | 2 × 100 = 200 | 2 × 1000 = 2000 |

Notice how the place value changes, and remember that the '0' acts as a place-holder.

For harder calculations, like 2 × 30, we can think of this as 2 × 3 × 10, or 6 × 10 = 60.

Also, 2 × 300 = 600, and 2 × 3000 = 6000 – can you see why?

Read them aloud and it sounds logical:
2 times 3 hundred **equals 6** hundred.

Explain these multiplications to an adult: 4 × 6 = 24; 40 × 6 = 240; 4 × 60 = 240; 40 × 60 = 2400.

This will help you develop your mental maths with larger numbers and extend your times tables skills.

---

1 Answer these questions:

a. 10 × 12 =

b. 15 × 10 =

c. 30 × 3 =

d. 7 × 50 =

e. 7 × 100 =

f. 100 × 12 =

g. 5 × 300 =

h. 6 × 1000 =

i. 4 × 3000 =

Now try this

2 John says, "20 times 30 equals 60."
Can you explain his mistake to an adult?

3 If 30 children each give their teacher 70p in a collection, how much will there be altogether?

_____

Explain to an adult how you solved it.

Mentally multiplying larger numbers can be easier if we use our times tables.

For example, in 4 × 13, the 13 can be split into 10 and 3.

As the arrays show, we have 4 10s and 4 3s.

4 × 10 = 40 and 4 × 3 = 12

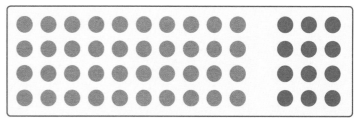

40 + 12 = 52

So, 4 × 13 = 52

Now look at this calculation: 42 × 6 = 252. How was it done?
Think about splitting 42 into 40 and 2...

---

1 Answer these questions:

a. 13 × 2 = ☐   **c.** 5 × 32 = ☐   **e.** 3 × 36 = ☐

b. 16 × 5 = ☐   **d.** 9 × 22 = ☐   **f.** 87 × 6 = ☐

2 Circle the correct answer for **12 × 25**:   275   300   325   350

Explain your thinking.

_____

3 Anita calculates correctly that 22 × 33 = 726. She did four separate multiplications and then added them together. Write down the four multiplications.

_____

_____

What is the most complicated <u>mental multiplication</u> you can do? Challenge an adult – tell them that they must explain their methods!

Ratio compares amounts. This pattern has one orange square to three white squares. The ratio of orange to white is 1 : 3.

We can use times tables facts with ratio. If this pattern was extended so that there were four orange squares, we can calculate that there will be 4 × 3 = 12 white squares.

Or, if it was extended to create 18 white squares, we know that there will be 18 ÷ 3 = 6 orange squares.

Scale is the difference in size between two things, such as models and real things. Scale is shown as a ratio.

John makes a model of his house. He makes it at a scale of 1 : 50, this means 1cm of the model represents 50cm of the house, or $\frac{1}{2}$ m.

So, a 12cm model at a scale of 1 : 50 will represent a 12 × 50 = 600cm, or 6m tall house.

Algebra is a bit different. It uses letters instead of numbers. These letters always represent a number. For example, in the expression $k + 2 = 3$, the letter k must equal 1.

This works for multiplication too, where we can use times tables facts to help us.

These algebra problems are a bit like missing number problems.

In the algebraic expression $6f = 30$, f must equal 5 because 6 × 5 = 30. (Notice that we do not include a multiplication sign, we don't say $6 × f = 30$, just $6f = 30$.)

1 The ratio of packed lunches to school dinners is 1 : 7. Complete the chart to help the school's cook work out how many dinners to prepare.

Number of packed lunches	3	5	6	7	8	11	15	25
Number of dinners needed	21							

2 Jemma creates statue animals at a scale of 8 : 3. Complete the chart.

> You will need to divide by 8 then multiply by 3.

Height of animal	16cm	64cm	80cm	240cm	320cm	400cm
Height of statue						

3 Use your times tables to find the value of each of these letters.

a. $5m = 55$, $m =$ ⬚

b. $6w = 54$, $w =$ ⬚

c. $3j + 1 = 7$, $j =$ ⬚

d. $7 - 2q = 1$, $q =$ ⬚

4 In the algebraic expression $xy = 24$, x and y can have different values. Can you complete this chart?

x	1						
y	24						

**Play this game with an adult. Take turns to call out a an algebraic expression, for example "3x = 15".
Your partner must say what x is.**

14 Multi-step problems

The main thing we do with mathematics is to use it in everyday situations: counting money, weighing things, and so on.

> *Oranges cost 6p each, so 7 oranges will cost 7 × 6 = 42p.*

Sometimes, the problems we have to solve require more than one step.

> *Oranges cost 6p each and I buy 7. If I give the shopkeeper £1, how much change will I receive?*

First, calculate the cost of the oranges. 7 × 6 = 42p; then do a subtraction: 100 − 42 = 58p.

Notice that £1 had to be changed to 100p.

There can even be three-step problems:

6p   8p

> *Oranges cost 6p each; pears cost 8p each.*
> *If I buy 4 oranges and 5 pears, how much change will I receive from £1?*

See if you can follow the calculation:

4 × 6 + 5 × 8 = 64;

100 − 64 = 36p change.

> **You may need to use more than one type of calculation.**

Solve these multi-step problems.

Use a separate piece of paper for your calculations if you need to.

1   A bag of nuts has a mass of 50g and a bag of raisins, 200g.

    What is the total mass of 7 bags of nuts and 6 bags of raisins?

2   A lawn is 6m wide and 9m long, with a flowerbed
in the middle that is 3m long and 2m wide.

Calculate the area of the lawn.

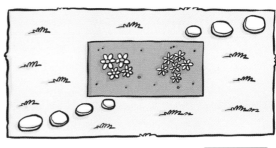

3   A fruit shop is having a sale. Calculate four different
combinations of fruit that you could buy for exactly £2.
The maximum for any one type of fruit is 12 items.

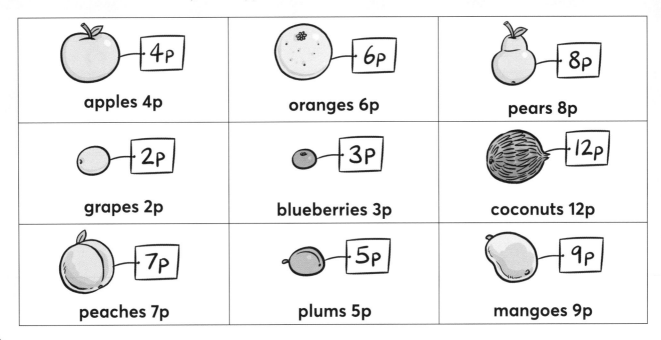

apples 4p	oranges 6p	pears 8p
grapes 2p	blueberries 3p	coconuts 12p
peaches 7p	plums 5p	mangoes 9p

Write your choices here. Use separate paper for calculations if you need to.

1. _____

2. _____

3. _____

4. _____

Start with £1.44. Choose a number from the times tables and
subtract it from 144. Next, tell your partner how much change you
received. They must then tell you how many items you bought, and
for how much, for example "You received 99p change, so you
could have bought 5 mangoes for 9p each. £1.44 – 45p = 99p".

Every question and problem on these two pages requires you to use times tables facts to solve it. Try to use these points to think about your approach to problem solving.

For each new problem, ask yourself:

- What am I being asked to do?

- What maths do I need to do it?

- Can I make or draw anything to help?

- Does my answer look 'about right'?

- How can I check my work?

> **Remember, to solve multi-step problems you may have to do more than one type of calculation.**

Solve these problems. Use a separate piece of paper for your calculations if you need to.

1 A head teacher wants the children in her school to make a donation to a wildlife charity. There are 500 children in the school.

She calculates how much the school would raise depending on the donation made.

a. Complete the chart. Remember that there is 100p in £1.

Donation per child	5p	6p	7p	8p	9p	10p	11p	12p	20p
Total raised in £									

b. What is the minimum that each child must donate to raise over £40?

2 A pack of ten biscuits costs 23p.

Josh needs 120 biscuits for the Year 6 leaving party.

Calculate how much change he will get from £5.

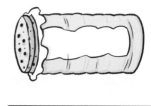

3 The ratio of cats to dogs in a town is 6 : 7.

If there are 420 cats, how many cats and dogs are there altogether?

_____

4 A scale model of a tower is 12cm high.

If the scale of the model is 1 : 125 calculate how tall the actual tower is.

[   ]

5 Use your times tables to find the value of each of these letters.

a. $3x = 27$, $x =$ [   ]

b. $7x + 2 = 23$, $x =$ [   ]

c. $80 - 9x = 17$, $x =$ [   ]

d. $2y + 2 = 10$, $y =$ [   ]

e. $6t + 7 = 37$, $t =$ [   ]

> **With a partner, take turns to choose a times tables fact, such as 7 × 6 = 42. Your partner must then invent a question to suit the fact, such as "There are 6 eggs in every box. How many eggs in 7 boxes?" Can you cover all the different problem-solving areas in this book?**

This is a game for 2 players.

You will need:

Two sets of counters or pieces of paper. Each set must be a different colour.

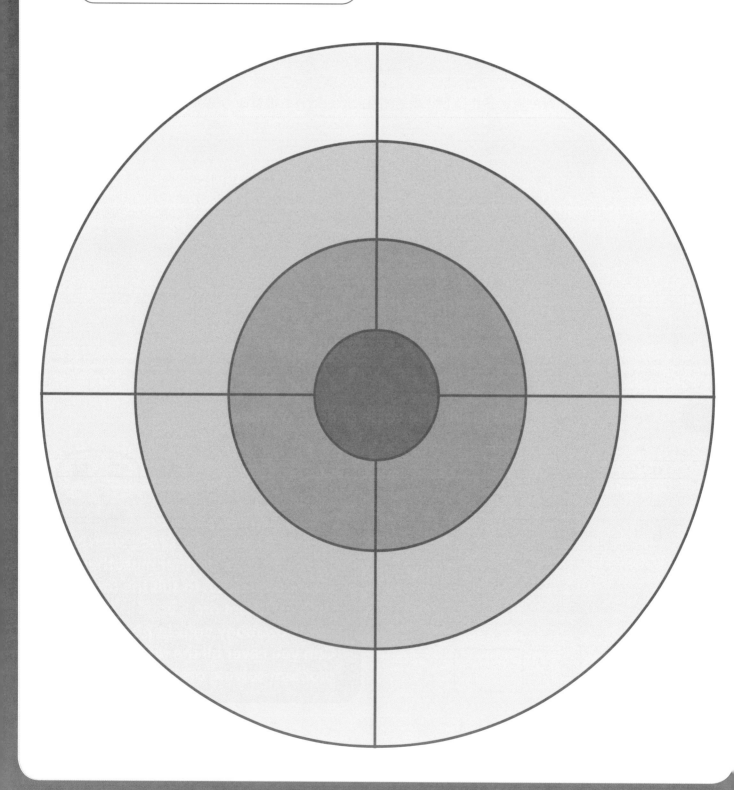

- The object of the game is to be the first player to have a counter on every sector of the target. (Both players can put one counter on each sector.)

- There are 13 sectors altogether – 4 in each of the three rings and 1 in the centre.

- Players choose their counters (or colour in 13 pieces of paper), then take turns.

- Whoever goes first says which sector on the target they choose. Depending on the sector they choose, their opponent must make up a question. The numbers of the sectors are difficulty levels:

4	Any times tables question (such as 8 × 6)
3	Any multiple of 10 multiplied by a single digit (such as 70 × 5, or 8 × 30)
2	Any multiple of 10 multiplied by another multiple of 10 (such as 40 × 70, or 80 × 30)
1	Any 2-digit number multiplied by any number from 1 to 12 (such as 34 × 6, or 5 × 42)

- Players must answer using mental maths only – the first answer given is the only answer accepted. Both players check the answer.

- Set a time limit per question for greater tension!

- If the answer is correct, add a counter. If it is wrong, try again on your next turn.

- The first player to get a counter on every sector shouts **BULLSEYE!**

Mixed tables test: mega tables

TEST 1

a. 4 × ☐ = 40

b. 3 × ☐ = 150

c. 2 × ☐ = 60

d. 5 × ☐ = 400

e. 9 × ☐ = 360

f. 1 × ☐ = 120

g. 9 × ☐ = 630

h. 6 × ☐ = 600

i. ☐ × 30 = 180

j. ☐ × 60 = 660

k. ☐ × 70 = 140

l. ☐ × 60 = 720

TEST 2

a. 40 × 5 = ☐

b. ☐ × 20 = 160

c. 30 × ☐ = 90

d. 5 × 50 = ☐

e. 7 × ☐ = 630

f. 80 × 4 = ☐

g. ☐ × 90 = 270

h. 8 × 60 = ☐

i. ☐ × 20 = 400

j. 50 × 70 = ☐

k. 80 × ☐ = 4000

l. 90 × 90 = ☐

TEST 3

a. 30 × 10 = ☐

b. 90 × 60 = ☐

c. 10 × 110 = ☐

d. 20 × 80 = ☐

e. 80 × ☐ = 6400

f. 70 × ☐ = 2100

g. 90 × ☐ = 1800

h. 60 × ☐ = 3000

i. ☐ ÷ 2 = 20

j. ☐ ÷ 7 = 50

k. ☐ ÷ 6 = 60

l. ☐ ÷ 8 = 110

Don't be scared by powers of 10!

Quick tests

Use these tests to assess your progress. They are all the same difficulty level. Ask an adult to time you.

TEST 1

1. 2 × 11 =

2. 3 × 6 =

3. 6 × 2 =

4. 7 × 10 =

5. 5 × 5 =

6. 9 × 4 =

7. 8 × 3 =

8. 6 × 7 =

9. 9 × 9 =

10. 12 × 4 =

11. 9 × 6 =

12. 5 × 12 =

13. 10 × [ ] = 100

14. 7 × 2 =

15. 4 × 4 =

16. 6 × 8 =

17. 9 ÷ 3 =

18. 80 ÷ 8 =

19. 24 ÷ 12 =

20. 40 ÷ 5 =

21. 18 ÷ 2 =

22. 5 × [ ] = 35

23. 3 × [ ] = 36

24. 6 × [ ] = 24

25. 9 × [ ] = 27

Mark: [ ] **out of 25**

TEST 2

1. 3 × 4 =

2. 6 × 5 =

3. 10 × 9 =

4. 5 × 2 =

5. 6 × 6 =

6. 6 × 11 =

7. 3 × 5 =

8. 11 × 10 =

9. 4 × 12 =

10. 5 × 9 =

11. 3 × 7 =

12. 4 × 6 =

13. 11 × [ ] = 132

14. 12 × 12 =

15. 11 × 11 =

16. 9 × 1 =

17. 44 ÷ 4 =

18. 84 ÷ 7 =

19. 36 ÷ 3 =

20. 16 ÷ 8 =

21. 30 ÷ 10 =

22. 4 × [ ] = 36

23. 6 × [ ] = 60

24. 2 × [ ] = 16

25. 7 × [ ] = 56

Mark: [ ] **out of 25**

Quick tests

Can you improve your time for each test?

TEST 3

1. $10 \times 5 =$

2. $2 \times 2 =$

3. $2 \times 10 =$

4. $8 \times 6 =$

5. $12 \times 1 =$

6. $2 \times 5 =$

7. $8 \times 12 =$

8. $7 \times 4 =$

9. $2 \times 7 =$

10. $3 \times 11 =$

11. $7 \times 7 =$

12. $3 \times 2 =$

13. $12 \times \boxed{} = 108$

14. $8 \times 10 =$

15. $9 \times 7 =$

16. $12 \times 8 =$

17. $18 \div 6 =$

18. $88 \div 11 =$

19. $27 \div 3 =$

20. $24 \div 2 =$

21. $15 \div 5 =$

22. $7 \times \boxed{} = 42$

23. $4 \times \boxed{} = 20$

24. $9 \times \boxed{} = 72$

25. $8 \times \boxed{} = 56$

Mark: ☐ out of 25

TEST 4

1. $4 \times 2 =$

2. $12 \times 10 =$

3. $4 \times 3 =$

4. $8 \times 4 =$

5. $11 \times 5 =$

6. $3 \times 8 =$

7. $7 \times 3 =$

8. $5 \times 4 =$

9. $12 \times 6 =$

10. $8 \times 8 =$

11. $4 \times 7 =$

12. $12 \times 11 =$

13. $7 \times \boxed{} = 35$

14. $9 \times 11 =$

15. $10 \times 4 =$

16. $8 \times 9 =$

17. $66 \div 11 =$

18. $72 \div 6 =$

19. $54 \div 9 =$

20. $45 \div 9 =$

21. $63 \div 7 =$

22. $10 \times \boxed{} = 70$

23. $5 \times \boxed{} = 60$

24. $8 \times \boxed{} = 88$

25. $5 \times \boxed{} = 40$

Mark: ☐ out of 25

Progress chart

Work through one unit at a time before moving on to the next one.

Making progress? Tick (✔) the circles as you complete each section of the book.

1 Multiplication ◯

2 Linking multiplication and division ◯

3 Revising the 2-, 5- and 10-times tables ◯

4 Revising the 3-, 6- and 9-times tables ◯

5 Revising the 4-, 8- and 12-times tables ◯

6 Revising the 7- and 11-times tables ◯

7 Patterns in the tables ◯

8 Number walls ◯

9 Factors and multiples ◯

10 Squares and primes ◯

11 Multiplying powers of ten ◯

12 Multiplying 2-digit numbers ◯

13 Ratio, scale and algebra ◯

14 Multi-step problems ◯

15 Mixed practice ◯

Well Done!

Answers

Unit	Question number	Answers
1 Multiplication pages 6–7	1	a. 3 × 4 = 12 b. 5 × 8 = 40
	2	Allow any suitable explanation that links the idea of repeated addition to multiplication.
	3	6 rows of 2 3 rows of 4 4 rows of 3 1 row of 12 12 rows of 1
	4	4 × 3 = 12 **OR** 3 × 4 = 12
2 Linking multiplication and division pages 8–9	1	a. 4 books b. 10 sheep
	2	a. 3 × 4 = 12 horseshoes b. 40 ÷ 4 = 10 people
	3	
3 Revising the 2-, 5- and 10-times tables pages 10–11	1	
	2	a. 10, 20 c. 10, 20, 30, 40, 50, 60 b. 10, 20 d. 10, 20
	3	a. Top: Rangers20 c. 14 points more b. Bottom: City

Unit	Question number	Answers
4 Revising the 3-, 6- and 9-times tables pages 12–13	1	
	2	**3**: The digit in the 1s place works through every digit before repeating themselves. **6**: The digit in the 1s place repeats the pattern 6, 2, 8, 4, 0. **9**: The digits for each fact add up to 9 and the 10s number is 1 less than the number which 9 is multiplied by (7 × 9 = 63).
	3	The highest number of aliens from each planet that can receive contact lenses is 16, with 12 lenses left over. Method: Find 12 of each for 3, 6, 9 then look at other numbers and add these to the 12s until the total is under 300. 12 × 3 = 36 and 4 × 3 = 12; 36 + 12 = 48 lenses for planet Bim 12 × 6 = 72 and 4 × 6 = 24; 72 + 24 = 96 for planet Bam 12 × 9 = 108 and 4 × 9 = 36; 108 + 36 = 144 for planet Bom Total: 288 lenses
	4	Each part has the same answer: 12 × 3 = 36 6 × 6 = 36 3 × 12 = 36 so 12 × 3 = 6 × 6 = 3 × 12
Mixed tables test: 2, 3, 5, 6, 9, 10 page 15	1	a. 2 × 6 = **12** g. 3 × **8** = 24 b. 2 × 8 = **16** h. 10 × **10** = 100 c. 6 × **5** = 30 i. 2 × **4** = 8 d. 10 × 9 = **90** j. 3 × 4 = **12** e. 5 × 3 = **15** k. 5 × **7** = 35 f. 6 × 1 = **6** l. 3 × **12** = 36
	2	a. 10 × **5** = 50 g. 5 × **5** = 25 b. 3 × 11 = **33** h. 6 × 6 = **36** c. 2 × **10** = 20 i. 9 × 5 = **45** d. 2 × **3** = 6 j. 6 × **3** = 18 e. 10 × 4 = **40** k. 6 × 8 = **48** f. 9 × **4** = 36 l. 9 × 12 = **108**
	3	a. 9 × 9 = 81 g. 10 × 3 = 30 b. 5 × 8 = **40** h. 9 × 6 = **54** c. 2 × 11 = 22 i. 6 × 12 = 72 d. 3 × **6** = 18 j. 2 × 12 = **24** e. 3 × 9 = **27** k. 5 × **12** = 60 f. 5 × **4** = 20 l. **10** × 12 = 120
5 Revising the 4-, 8- and 12-times tables pages 16–17	1	a. 4, 8, 12, 16, 20, **24**, **28**, **32**, **36**, **40** b. 8, 16, 24, 32, 40, **48**, **56**, **64**, **72**, **80** c. 12, 24, 36, 48, 60, **72**, **84**, **96**, **108**, **120**
	2	a. 8, 16, 24, 32, 40, 48 b. 12, 24, 36, 48 c. 24, 48, 72, 96
	3	Show your friend that the 8-times table is double the 4-times table.
	4	The easiest way is selling 9 of each shell. The shells added together cost £24 and 9 x 24 = 216. **OR** 11 £4 shells, 8 £8 shells, and 9 £12 shells gives 44 + 64 + 108 = 216. Many other answers are possible, such as 8 £4 shells, 8 £8 shells, and 10 £12 shells gives 32 + 64 + 120 = 216
6 Revising the 7- and 11-times tables pages 18–19	1	a. 7, 14, **21**, **28**, **35**, **42**, **49**, **56**, **63**, **70**, **77**, **84** b. 11, 22, **33**, **44**, **55**, **66**, **77**, **88**, **99**, **110**, **121**, **132**
	2	Because multiplication is commutative their multiples appear twice on the times tables square ie 2 × 7 = 14 and 7 × 2 = 14.
	3	The school could send 11 teams for each sport (121 + 77 with 2 children left over).

Unit	Question number	Answers
Mixed tables test: 4, 7, 8, 11, 12 page 21	1	**a.** 4 × 6 = **24** **g.** 4 × **12** = 48 **b.** 8 × **3** = 24 **h.** 7 × **6** = 42 **c.** 8 × 4 = **32** **i.** 11 × **11** = 121 **d.** 7 × 9 = **63** **j.** 11 × 1 = **11** **e.** 7 × **7** = 49 **k.** 12 × **7** = 84 **f.** 8 × 8 = **64** **l.** 12 × 3 = **36**
	2	**a.** 7 × **5** = 35 **g.** 4 × 9 = **36** **b.** 8 × **5** = 40 **h.** 11 × 9 = **99** **c.** 7 × 3 = **21** **i.** 4 × **3** = 12 **d.** 12 × **8** = 96 **j.** 12 × 5 = **60** **e.** 8 × 11 = 88 **k.** 8 × 10 = **80** **f.** 4 × 10 = **40** **l.** 11 × **4** = 44
	3	**a.** **4** × 7 = 28 **g.** 8 × 6 = **48** **b.** 11 × **7** = 77 **h.** 12 × **6** = 72 **c.** 12 × 2 = **24** **i.** **7** × 10 = 70 **d.** **11** × 3 = 33 **j.** **8** × 9 = 72 **e.** 7 × 2 = **14** **k.** 4 × **5** = 20 **f.** **7** × 8 = 56 **l.** 11 × 12 = **132**
7 Patterns in the tables pages 22–23	1	18 has two different 'partner facts': 2 × 9 and 9 × 2, and 3 × 6 and 6 × 3. 16, however, has only one pair of partners: 2 × 8 and 8 × 2, and one 'diagonal fact': 4 × 4.
	2	There are 36 odd numbers on the times tables square. The odd numbers are every other square going across and down. There are fewer odd numbers than even numbers as only an odd number × an odd number has an odd product, such as 3 × 5 = 15. Even numbers can be made by multiplying even × even or even × odd. There are six odd numbers between 1 and 12, and they all multiply each other once so 6 × 6 = 36 odd numbers altogether.
	3	**a.** 12, 24; 6 times **b.** 6, 8, 10, 18, 20, 30, 40, 48, 60, 72 **c.** 1, 25, 49, 64, 81, 100, 121, 144 **d.** 13, 17, 19, 23, 26, 29, 31
	4	1 shelf: 24 books; 2 shelves: 12 books; 3 shelves: 8 books; 4 shelves: 6 books; 6 shelves: 4 books; 8 shelves: 3 books; 12 shelves: 2 books; 24 shelves: 1 book
8 Number walls pages 24–25	1	3 × 8; 4 × 6; 6 × 4; 8 × 3; 2 × 12
	2	<table><tr><td>2</td><td>2</td><td>2</td><td>2</td><td>2</td><td>2</td><td>2</td><td>2</td><td>2</td><td>2</td></tr><tr><td colspan="2">5</td><td colspan="2">5</td><td colspan="3">5</td><td colspan="3">5</td></tr><tr><td colspan="5">10</td><td colspan="5">10</td></tr></table>
	3	4 × 12cm = 48cm Cost for 4 12cm tiles = 4 × £10 = £40 6 × 8cm = 48cm Cost for 6 8cm tiles = 6 × £9 = £54 8 × 6cm= 48cm Cost for 8 6cm tiles = 8 × £8 = £64 There are 3 4s in 12, so there will be 4 × 3 = 12 4s in 48. Cost = 12 × £7 = £84 There are 4 3s in 12, so there will be 4 × 4 = 16 3s in 48. Cost = 16 × £6 = £96 There are 6 2s in 12, so there will be 4 × 6 = 24 2s in 48. Cost = 24 × £5 = £120 • The cheapest option is: 4 12cm tiles on the bottom; then 6 8cm tiles; then 8 6cm tiles; then 12 4cm tiles. Total cost = £40 + £54 + £ 64 + £84 = £242 • The most expensive option is: 8 6cm tiles; then 12 4cm tiles; then 16 3cm tiles; then 24 2cm tiles. Total cost = £64 + £84 + £96 + £120 = £364

Unit	Question number	Answers
9 Factors and multiples pages 26–27	1	**a. 2**, **4**: 8, 12, ⟨22⟩ 28 **d. 8**, **12**: 24, ⟨56⟩ 72, 96 **b. 3**, **7**: 21, ⟨35⟩ 42, 63 **e. 3**, **11**: 33, 66, ⟨88⟩ 132 **c. 6**, **10**: 30, 60, 90, ⟨110⟩ **f. 4**, **6**: 12, ⟨18⟩ 24, 48
	2	**a.** 6: 1, 6; 2, 3 **e.** 30: 3, 10; 5, 6 **b.** 11: 1, 11 **f.** 48: 4, 12; 6, 8 **c.** 15: 3, 5 **g.** 60: 6, 10; 5, 12 **d.** 16: 2, 8; 4, 4 **h.** 99: 9, 11
	3	21 (3 and 7); 22 (2 and 11); 27 (3 and 9); 28 (4 and 7) 24 has six factors (2, 12, 3, 8, 4, 6); 25 only has 1 factor (5); 23, 26 and 29 are not on the grid.
	4	12: 1, 12; 2, 6; 3, 4 or 24: 2, 12; 3, 8; 4, 6 Answers can vary: they occur in fewer times tables; they are square numbers; they are prime numbers.
10 Squares and primes pages 28–29	1	<table><tr><th>Times table</th><th>Square</th><th>Using the ²</th><th>=</th></tr><tr><td>1 ×</td><td>1 × 1</td><td>1^2</td><td>1</td></tr><tr><td>2 ×</td><td>**2 × 2**</td><td>**2^2**</td><td>**4**</td></tr><tr><td>3 ×</td><td>**3 × 3**</td><td>**3^2**</td><td>**9**</td></tr><tr><td>4 ×</td><td>**4 × 4**</td><td>**4^2**</td><td>**16**</td></tr><tr><td>5 ×</td><td>**5 × 5**</td><td>**5^2**</td><td>**25**</td></tr><tr><td>6 ×</td><td>**6 × 6**</td><td>**6^2**</td><td>**36**</td></tr><tr><td>7 ×</td><td>**7 × 7**</td><td>**7^2**</td><td>**49**</td></tr><tr><td>8 ×</td><td>**8 × 8**</td><td>**8^2**</td><td>**64**</td></tr><tr><td>9 ×</td><td>**9 × 9**</td><td>**9^2**</td><td>**81**</td></tr><tr><td>10 ×</td><td>**10 × 10**</td><td>**10^2**</td><td>**100**</td></tr><tr><td>11 ×</td><td>**11 × 11**</td><td>**11^2**</td><td>**121**</td></tr><tr><td>12 ×</td><td>**12 × 12**</td><td>**12^2**</td><td>**144**</td></tr></table>
	2	They are in a diagonal line.
	3	A hundred grid with all composite numbers crossed out. The remaining numbers on the grid are all prime numbers.
	4	101, 103, 107, 109

Unit	Question number	Answers
Mixed tables test: all tables page 31	1	a. 4 × 8 = **32** g. 4 × **2** = 8 b. 6 × **7** = 42 h. 5 × **6** = 30 c. 9 × 7 = **63** i. 12 × **12** = 144 d. 2 × 7 = **14** j. 8 × 1 = **8** e. 9 × **8** = 72 k. 11 × 2 = **22** f. 8 × 2 = **16** l. 10 × **6** = 60
	2	a. 4 × **4** = 16 g. 8 × **7** = 56 b. 5 × 9 = **45** h. 7 × 12 = **84** c. 12 × **4** = 48 i. 2 × **9** = 18 d. 3 × **7** = 21 j. 12 × 11 = **132** e. 12 × 10 = **120** k. 6 × 4 = **24** f. 1 × **12** = 12 l. 3 × 3 = **9**
	3	a. **54** ÷ 6 = 9 g. 110 ÷ **10** = 11 b. 15 ÷ **3** = 5 h. **99** ÷ 11 = 9 c. 12 ÷ 2 = **6** i. 7 ÷ **1** = 7 d. **77** ÷ 11 = 7 j. **5** ÷ 1 = 5 e. **108** ÷ 9 = 12 k. 96 ÷ **12** = 8 f. 28 ÷ 7 = **4** l. **27** ÷ 9 = 3
11 Multiplying powers of 10 page 32	1	a. 120 d. 350 g. 1500 b. 150 e. 700 h. 6000 c. 90 f. 1200 i. 12,000
	2	He has either calculated 2 × 30 OR 3 × 20 OR he has not used place value correctly. (2 × 3 × 10 × 10 = 600)
	3	30 × 70p = 3 × 7 × 10 × 10 = 21 × 100 = 2100p = £21
12 Multiplying 2-digit numbers page 33	1	a. 26 c. 160 e. 108 b. 80 d. 198 f. 522
	2	300 (12 × 25 is 10 × 25 + 2 × 25, which is 250 + 50 = 300)
	3	20 × 30 = 600, 20 × 3 = 60, 2 × 30 = 60, 2 × 3 = 6
13 Ratio, scale and algebra pages 34–35	1	Number of dinners needed 	21	**35**	**42**	**49**	**56**	**77**	**105**	**175**	
	2	Height of statue 	**6cm**	**24cm**	**30cm**	**90cm**	**120cm**	**150cm**	
	3	a. $m = 11$ b. $w = 9$ c. $j = 2$ d. $q = 3$
	4		**x**	1	2	3	4	6	8	12	24
y	24	12	8	6	4	3	2	1	
14 Multi-step problems pages 36–37	1	The total mass of seven bags of nuts and six bags of raisins is 1550g. 7 × 50 = 350 6 × 200 = 1200 200 + 350 = 1550g OR 1.55kg
	2	6 × 9 − 2 × 3 = 48m²
	3	Example answers: 12 apples, 12 oranges, 10 pears (12 × 4 + 12 × 6 + 10 × 8: 48 + 72 + 80 = £2) 10 coconuts, 5 peaches, 9 plums (10 × 12 + 5 × 7 + 9 × 5: 120 + 35 + 45 = £2) 12 mangoes, 12 plums, 10 blueberries, 1 grape (12 × 9 + 12 × 5 + 10 × 3 + 1 × 2: 108 + 60 + 30 + 2 = £2)

Unit	Question number	Answers
15 Mixed practice pages 38–39	1	Total raised in £ | £25	£30	£35	£40	£45	£50	£55	£60	£100 | The minimum that each child must donate to raise over £40 is 9p
	2	500 − 276 = £2.24 change
	3	420 cats + 490 dogs = 910 pets
	4	12 × 125 = 12 × 120 + 12 × 5 = 1440 + 60 = 1500cm or 15m
	5	a. $3x = 27$, $x =$ **9** b. $7x + 2 = 23$, $x =$ **3** c. $80 − 9x = 17$, $x =$ **7** d. $2y + 2 = 10$, $y =$ **4** e. $6t + 7 = 37$, $t =$ **5**
Mixed tables test: mega tables page 42	1	a. 4 × **10** = 40 g. 9 × **70** = 630 b. 3 × **50** = 150 h. 6 × **100** = 600 c. 2 × **30** = 60 i. **6** × 30 = 180 d. 5 × **80** = 400 j. **11** × 60 = 660 e. 9 × **40** = 360 k. **2** × 70 = 140 f. 1 × **120** = 120 l. **12** × 60 = 720
	2	a. 40 × 5 = **200** g. 3 × 90 = 270 b. **8** × 20 = 160 h. 8 × 60 = **480** c. 30 × 3 = 90 i. **20** × 20 = 400 d. 5 × 50 = **250** j. 50 × 70 = **3500** e. 7 × **90** = 630 k. 80 × **50** = 4000 f. 80 × 4 = **320** l. 90 × 90 = **8100**
	3	a. 30 × 10 = **300** g. 90 × **20** = 1800 b. 90 × 60 = **5400** h. 60 × **50** = 3000 c. 10 × 110 = **1100** i. **40** ÷ 2 = 20 d. 20 × 80 = **1600** j. **350** ÷ 7 = 50 e. 80 × 80 = 6400 k. **360** ÷ 6 = 60 f. 70 × 30 = 2100 l. **880** ÷ 8 = 110
Quick tests pages 43–44	Test 1	1. 22 8. 42 15. 16 22. 7 2. 18 9. 81 16. 48 23. 12 3. 12 10. 48 17. 3 24. 4 4. 70 11. 54 18. 10 25. 3 5. 25 12. 60 19. 2 6. 36 13. 10 20. 8 7. 24 14. 14 21. 9
	Test 2	1. 12 8. 110 15. 121 22. 9 2. 30 9. 48 16. 9 23. 10 3. 90 10. 45 17. 11 24. 8 4. 10 11. 21 18. 12 25. 8 5. 36 12. 24 19. 12 6. 66 13. 12 20. 2 7. 15 14. 144 21. 3
	Test 3	1. 50 8. 28 15. 63 22. 6 2. 4 9. 14 16. 96 23. 5 3. 20 10. 33 17. 3 24. 8 4. 48 11. 49 18. 8 25. 7 5. 12 12. 6 19. 9 6. 10 13. 9 20. 12 7. 96 14. 80 21. 3
	Test 4	1. 8 8. 20 15. 40 22. 7 2. 120 9. 72 16. 72 23. 12 3. 12 10. 64 17. 6 24. 11 4. 32 11. 28 18. 12 25. 8 5. 55 12. 121 19. 6 6. 24 13. 5 20. 5 7. 21 14. 99 21. 9